KU-500-479

How Many Ducks Could Fit in a Bus?

CREATIVE WAYS TO LOOK AT VOLUME

Clara Cella

raintree
a Capstone company — publishers for children

How many ducks
could fit in a
bus without
any flapping,
quacking
or fuss?

7 ducks!

Could baby **birds** fit in a cup this small? YES! Turn the page! Let's count them all!

Squeal!
Squeeeeeeal!
Rub-a-dub-dub!
How many
piglets could
fit in a tub?

5 piglets!

Look at
this
doughnut.
Try not to drool!
How many
doughnuts fit
in a paddling pool?

8 doughnuts!

This square **box** has lots to hide. How many turtles fit inside?

FRESH

Next comes
a sweet,
count-along treat:
a spoonful of
honeybees
you can eat!

How many **fish** could fit in here, swimming in water cool and clear?

**10
fish!**

How many **raccoons** are sharing your lunch?

6

The basket is
full, so I'd say
A BUNCH!

LOOK FOR OTHER BOOKS IN THE SERIES:

How Many Flamingos Tall Is a Giraffe?
CREATIVE WAYS TO LOOK AT HEIGHT
by Clara Cella

How Many Kittens Could Ride a Shark?
CREATIVE WAYS TO LOOK AT LENGTH
by Clara Cella

How Many Llamas Does a Car Weigh?
CREATIVE WAYS TO LOOK AT WEIGHT
by Clara Cella

Raintree is an imprint of Capstone Global Library Limited, a company incorporated in England and Wales having its registered office at 264 Banbury Road, Oxford, OX2 7DY – Registered company number: 6695582

www.raintree.co.uk
myorders@raintree.co.uk

Edited by Jill Kalz
Designed by Ted Williams
Media Researcher: Svetlana Zhurkin
Production Specialist: Katy LaVigne
Cover illustration by Giuliano Aloisi
Original illustrations © Capstone Global Library Limited 2021
Originated by Capstone Global Library Ltd
Printed and bound in India

ISBN: 978 1 4747 9532 6 (hardback)
ISBN: 978 1 4747 9714 6 (paperback)

British Library Cataloguing in Publication Data
A full catalogue record for this book is available from the British Library.

Acknowledgements
We would like to thank the following for permission to reproduce photographs:Capstone Studio: Karon Dubke, 23, 24, 25; Shutterstock: Africa Studio, 4–5 (room), Alison Henley, 7, 8–9, Andrey Armyagov, 28–29 (fish), Anton Starikov, 24–25 (spoon), Autobahn, 15, 16, 17, ben bryant, 12–13 (bathtub), dibrova, 5 (middle right), ESB Professional, cover (bus), back cover, Flashon Studio, 3, 4–5, Gerald A. DeBoer, 20 (turtles), 21 (bottom), grynold, 16–17 (pool), limpido, 27, 28–29, LittlePerfectStock, 11, 13 (top middle), Michiel de Wit, 21 (top), Sergei Kardashev, 20–21 (box), Sloth Astronaut, 19 (pizza slice logo), spawn101, cover (flower), 1, Tsekhmister, 5 (middle left), 12 (top middle), Viktar Savanevich, 8–9 (baby birds), vincent noel, 19, 20–21 (pizza logo), yevgeniy11, cover (duckling), 1, 4 (middle right), 12 (bottom middle), 13 (bottom middle), Yuliia Sonsedska, 4 (middle left), 13 (bottom right), 31 (raccoons), Yuri Samsonov, 30, 31.

Every effort has been made to contact copyright holders of material reproduced in this book. Any omissions will be rectified in subsequent printings if notice is given to the publisher.